ORS
CART
AND THE
SEA MONSTER

Steve Donald

RED FOX

To Nita

A Red Fox Book
Published by Random House Children's Books
20 Vauxhall Bridge Road, London SW1V 2SA

A division of Random House UK Ltd.
London Melbourne Sydney Auckland
Johannesburg and agencies throughout the world

First published by Hutchinson Children's Books 1993

Red Fox edition 1993

Printed and bound in Great Britain
by Cox & Wyman Ltd, Reading

ISBN 0 09 916281 4

CHAPTER ONE TRAINS, TICKETS AND TEASHOPS.

WHERE TO?
THE SEASIDE! YOU'RE GOING TO STAY WITH AUNTIE JILL AND UNCLE WALTER IN THEIR COTTAGE.

AREN'T YOU COMING?
I THINK IT'D BE NICE FOR YOU TO HAVE YOUR FIRST HOLIDAY WITHOUT US, DEAR.
MOP
DRY

WHEN?
AS SOON AS SCHOOL FINISHES.

GREAT! CAN I TAKE MY FRIENDS?
SORRY, SON. IT'S ONLY A TINY COTTAGE. YOU'LL MAKE FRIENDS THERE.

WOW! ALL BY MYSELF! MY OWN HOLIDAY!

A FEW DAYS LATER...
SAY HELLO TO AUNTIE JILL AND UNCLE WALTER! THEY'LL MEET YOU AT THE STATION.

AND TRY TO STAY IN ONE PIECE FOR A CHANGE!
YES, DAD.

AND DON'T STICK YOUR HEAD OUT OF THE TRAIN WINDOW LIKE THAT!
BYE!

TWO HOURS TO WINKLETHORPE-BY-SEA.
TIME TO READ A COMIC.
The BANDY

SUDDEN DRAUGHT
HEY!

COME BACK!

BUT-
OH NO!
NARROW TUNNEL

SMACK!

FIRST CLASS DINING CAR
AAAAAH!

SPLOSH!

VERY SORRY. I DIDN'T DRINK ANY. PROMISE!

MAY I SEE YOUR TICKET, SIR?

HERE IT COMES.

DO YOU HAVE A DINNER RESERVATION, SIR?
NO.

IN THAT CASE THERE WILL BE A £5 SURCHARGE FOR STICKING YOUR HEAD IN ANOTHER PASSENGER'S SOUP.
IT WAS AN ACCIDENT!

RULE NO. 1678 B: PENALTIES FOR THE MISUSE OF SOUP...
ALL RIGHT, THEN.

ORSON HAS NOTHING LEFT TO DO BUT PLAY NOUGHTS AND CROSSES WITH HIMSELF.

UNTIL-
BLIMEY!

WELCOME TO SUNNY
WINKLETHORPE-BY-SEA

AT THE STATION -
HELLO ORSON! MY, HAVEN'T YOU GROWN!
HELLO, AUNTIE JILL!
O.C.

WE'RE GLAD YOU MADE IT ALL RIGHT. YOUR MUM SEEMED A BIT WORRIED ON THE PHONE.
O.C.
REALLY? WHAT DID SHE SAY?
JUST THAT YOU WERE EVERYWHERE AT ONCE THESE DAYS.

ANYTHING ELSE?
NO. SHE JUST SAID IF YOU WERE ANY TROUBLE WE SHOULD TELL YOU TO PULL YOURSELF TOGETHER. DO YOU KNOW WHAT SHE MEANT?

NO IDEA.
WINK!
WELL, SHALL WE GET GOING, THEN?

BEFORE LONG -
THIS IS OUR COTTAGE.
GREAT!

NEXT MORNING-
I'M OFF TO WORK AT THE TEASHOP. WHY NOT COME ALONG?
O.K.

WE'D BETTER HURRY. MY BOSS, MR. SNITT, IS A REAL SLAVE-DRIVER. HE'LL BE ANGRY IF I'M LATE.

WHAT'S THAT OVER THERE?
AH. THAT'S THE MONASTERY.
SO DO MONKS LIVE THERE?
NOT NOW. IT'S JUST PART OF THE VIEW.

SOON-
YOU'RE LATE! YOU CAN STAY ON TONIGHT AND WASH DISHES!
SORRY, MR. SNITT. THIS IS MY NEPHEW ORSON.
OH, YES. WELL, I HOPE HE DOESN'T EXPECT TEA AND CAKES FOR NOTHING!
MENU

PERISH THE THOUGHT.
HE MAY BE YOUR NEPHEW BUT I'M THE MANAGER AND I SAY HE PAYS LIKE ANYONE ELSE. NOW GET TO WORK!

YES, BOSS.

WOULD YOU LIKE A NICE CUP OF TEA AND A SCONE, ORSON?
YES PLEASE. I'M STARVING.

GIVE HIM SOME OF MY OWN SPECIAL GINGER BEER. EVERYBODY SHOULD TRY IT. IT'S FAMOUS!
ALL RIGHT, BOSS.

SOON-
MMM, NICE. I'LL TRY THE GINGER BEER.

BUT-
UURGH!

ARE YOU HAVING THE GINGER BEER? DON'T! IT'S AWFUL!
SIZZLE SIZZLE

I KNOW. IT'S LIKE...
...LIKE GINGER FLAVOUR BATHWATER?

YES!
THANKS.
HERE, HAVE SOME OF MY LEMONADE. IT'LL WASH THE TASTE AWAY.

I'M STAYING WITH MY AUNT. SHE WORKS HERE.
WELL, I HOPE SHE DOESN'T MAKE THAT FOUL STUFF.

NO. MR. SNITT DOES.
HE SAYS IT'S FAMOUS.

FAMOUS FOR BEING HORRIBLE HE MEANS! PEOPLE COME FOR MILES JUST TO FIND OUT IF IT'S AS BAD AS THEY SAY – AND IT IS.

WHAT'S YOUR NAME?
KATE. WHAT'S YOURS?
ORSON.
THAT'S A FUNNY NAME!

IT'S ORSON CART.
HA HA! THAT'S EVEN FUNNIER!

WELL, YOU CAN LAUGH, BUT I BET I CAN BUILD A SANDCASTLE FASTER THAN YOU!
O.K. I'LL RACE YOU.

ON THE BEACH-
ON YOUR MARKS!
GET SET! GO!

DIG! DIG! DIG!

BUT-
ON YOUR MARKS!
GET SET! GO!
ZZIP!
CARVE!
SHAPE!
WHIZZ!
TROT!
DIG!
DIG!
DIG!

HOW DO YOU DO THAT?
OH, YOU JUST PAT THE SAND INTO THE BUCKET AND...
NO, HOW DO YOU TAKE YOUR HANDS OFF?
ORSON LETS KATE INTO HIS SECRET:
...WELL, THE LAWNMOWER THAT RAN ME OVER BELONGED TO A MAD PROFESSOR, AND HE STUCK ME BACK TOGETHER WITH SPECIAL GLUE, BUT BITS STILL COME OFF WHEN...

HEY, LOOK OUT! BEHIND YOU!
BLIMEY!

WHERE HAS THIS GIANT DINOSAUR COME FROM?

WHAT WILL IT DO TO ORSON AND KATE?

DOES THIS MEAN THE END OF THE SANDCASTLE RACE?

READ THE NEXT CHAPTER!

CHAPTER TWO MONSTERS, MONKS AND MYSTERY!

IT'S HEADING FOR THE CARAVAN SITE!
OH, NO! MY MUM AND DAD ARE UP THERE!

HEY! COME BACK! IT MIGHT EAT YOU!
IT MIGHT EAT MUM AND DAD!

RUMMAGE!
SNORT!
THAT'S OURS! STOP IT! GO AWAY! SHOO!

SCAT!
I THINK IT'S GOING.

MUM! DAD!

THEY'RE NOT HERE! DO YOU THINK IT'S EATEN THEM?
WHAT'S ALL THIS?

MUM! DAD!
YOU'RE NOT USUALLY THIS GLAD TO SEE US. DID YOU MAKE THIS MESS?

WE THOUGHT YOU'D BEEN EATEN!
NO. WE WENT OUT FOR AN ICE CREAM.

FOR GOODNESS SAKE, TIDY UP WHILE I PUT THE KETTLE ON. WHAT'S YOUR FRIEND'S NAME?
ORSON... BUT, YOU... ... THERE WAS...

WELL, ORSON, WE'LL HAVE SOME TEA AND BISCUITS, EH? WHERE ARE THOSE GINGER SNAPS? WE HAD A WHOLE PACKET. DID YOU EAT THEM?
NO.

WELL YOU'LL HAVE TO GO AND GET ME SOME MORE. OFF YOU GO, BOTH OF YOU.
PUSH

I DON'T THINK THEY BELIEVED US.
BELIEVED? THEY DIDN'T EVEN LISTEN.

WE'VE GOT TO INVESTIGATE THAT MONSTER! MAYBE IT'S A DINOSAUR THAT'S BEEN ALIVE FOR MILLIONS OF YEARS!

OR MAYBE WE DREAMED IT?
NO. LOOK WHAT IT DID TO MY SANDCASTLE!

COME ON! MUM WANTS SOME BISCUITS. WE CAN GET THEM FROM THE TEASHOP.

AND WE CAN INVESTIGATE WHILE WE'RE THERE!
TEAS

BACK AT THE TEASHOP:
A PACKET OF GINGER SNAPS, PLEASE, AUNTIE!
HERE YOU ARE. DID YOU HAVE A NICE TIME ON THE BEACH?

WE SAW A SEA MONSTER!
OH, REALLY? WHAT DID IT LOOK LIKE?

HUGE! WITH A LONG NECK!
AND BIG TEETH! IT WAS SCARY!

GOOD. THAT'S THIRTY PENCE FOR THE BISCUITS.
YOU DON'T BELIEVE US.

I THINK YOU'VE BEEN LISTENING TO THOSE TALL TALES THEY'RE TELLING IN THE VILLAGE.
BUT WE SAW IT!

SO WHERE IS IT NOW?
IT SWAM AWAY TOWARDS THE MONASTERY.

TOWARDS THE **MONASTERY**, YOU SAY?
MENU

TOWARDS THE OLD, RUINED MONASTERY ON THE CLIFFS?
Y- YES.

AAAAAAAGH! THAT MUST BE THE TERRIBLE SEA MONSTER THAT'S HAUNTED THESE PARTS FOR CENTURIES!

THEY SAY IT FRIGHTENED ALL THE MONKS AWAY! THAT'S WHY NOBODY GOES THERE!
DO YOU BELIEVE IN IT?

OH, YES! YOU'D BETTER BELIEVE IT. AND STAY AWAY FROM THERE!

THERE'S A TERRIBLE CURSE ON THAT PLACE. THEY SAY IF YOU GO THERE, YOU'LL NEVER COME BACK!
NEVER?

NEVER! AND IF YOU DO, YOU'LL HAVE MISSED SOMETHING REALLY GOOD ON THE TELLY, AND NO-ONE WILL HAVE VIDEOED IT! SO GOES THE MONSTER'S ANCIENT CURSE!
STEAM!

REMEMBER, STAY AWAY FROM THERE!
RIGHT, MR. SNITT.
RIGHT. FINE. BYE!
BYE, DEARS!
MENU

SO–
RIGHT, HERE WE ARE. LET'S LOOK AROUND.
OLD RUINED MONASTERY KEEP OUT
BY ORDER

NOT MUCH LEFT OF IT.
WHAT'S IT LIKE INSIDE?

THIS WAS A BIG ROOM. MAYBE IT WAS THE MONK'S DINING HALL.

WHERE TO NOW?
THE BEACH, I SUPPOSE.

WHAT'S THAT?
PROBABLY THE CELLAR.
OR A SMUGGLER'S TUNNEL. IT'S LOCKED, ANYWAY.

LOOK! DOWN THERE! A MONSTER FOOTPRINT!

HERE'S SOME MORE... AND WHAT'S THIS BROWN POWDER?
IT'S......IT'S GINGER BISCUIT CRUMBS!

THE MONSTER MUST HAVE TAKEN YOUR GINGER BISCUITS FROM THE CARAVAN!
WELL, NOW WE KNOW WHAT IT EATS!

A SEA MONSTER STOLE YOUR BISCUITS? – AND YOU ACTUALLY SAW IT?
YES! YES!

WELL, IT'S A GOOD JOKE, NO DOUBT, BUT I'VE HEARD IT TOO OFTEN TO SEE THE FUNNY SIDE.
BUT WE'RE NOT JOKING!

AARR, THAT'S WHAT THEY ALL SAY. I MUST HAVE HEARD THAT STORY ABOUT SEA MONSTERS STEALING GINGER BISCUITS A DOZEN TIMES!

IT'S AS BAD AS THEM CORN CIRCLES. I'LL BE LOOKING AT ONE CORN CIRCLE AND THEY'LL PINCH ME BIKE TO MAKE ANOTHER ONE WITH! CHEEKY LITTLE BLIGHTERS!

HE WASN'T VERY INTERESTED, WAS HE?
NO. BUT HE TOLD US SOMETHING.
WHAT?

THIS CREATURE GOES AROUND STEALING GINGER BISCUITS! IT'S DONE IT LOADS OF TIMES!

YES! AND THAT GIVES ME AN IDEA!
WHAT'S THAT, THEN?

A PLAN! I'LL GO AND GET OUR BUCKETS. WE'LL NEED TENT PEGS TOO. I KNOW WHERE TO GET THEM.
WHAT DO I DO?

GET THE BIGGEST SHEET OF CLOTH YOU CAN FIND. I'LL MEET YOU ON THE BEACH THERE.
WHAT FOR?

WE'RE GOING TO MAKE A MONSTER TRAP!

LATER-
WHERE DID YOU GET THAT?
IT'S A BOAT SAIL. I BORROWED IT DOWN AT THE HARBOUR.

NOW LET'S DIG A HOLE!

AAAK!
IS THAT BIG ENOUGH?
IF WE DIG ANY MORE, WE'LL COME OUT IN AUSTRALIA!

THEN-
GET IT NICE AND TAUT!

IS THAT ALL RIGHT?
YES! KEEP IT FLAT.
TAP TAP
TAP TAP

WITH THIS SAND ON, YOU CAN HARDLY SEE IT!
BUT IF YOU STOOD ON IT YOU'D FALL STRAIGHT IN. ESPECIALLY IF YOU WERE A TEN-TON SEA MONSTER!

WHAT IF IT DOESN'T STAND ON IT?
IT WILL. IT'LL COME FOR THESE BISCUITS!

NOW BE QUIET. WE DON'T WANT TO SCARE IT OFF.

ORSON!!

I'M GOING HOME NOW. I'M WORN OUT. LOOK AT YOU! YOU'D THINK YOU'D BEEN WORKING DOWN A PIT! BATHTIME FOR YOU!
BUT I'M BUSY!

AUNTIES! HUH! JUST WHEN YOU'RE GETTING TO WORK ON SOMETHING REALLY INTERESTING, THEY THINK YOU SHOULD BE HAVING A BATH!

AND SHE SAYS SHE'S GOING TO CHECK MY EARS ARE CLEAN. SUPPOSE I'D BETTER DO THEM.
POP!

TRICKY TO GET THE SAND OUT!
SCRUB! SCRUB!

SOON-
TIME FOR A QUICK TEA. I HOPE I DON'T MISS THE MONSTER GETTING CAUGHT!
GLUG! GLUG! GLUG!

BUT-
WHERE'S MY EAR? CRIKEY! MY LUGHOLE'S GONE DOWN THE PLUGHOLE!

I'VE GOT TO FIND IT! WHERE DOES THE WATER GO?
TWANG!
RRRIP!
CREAK!

COR! THAT'S NOT WHAT I EXPECTED!
GLORGLE!
GLUG!
WHERE DOES THE MYSTERIOUS TUNNEL GO?
WILL ORSON GET HIS EAR BACK?
WILL THE SEA MONSTER GET CAUGHT?
FIND OUT
IN-

CHAPTER THREE: Buckets, Biscuits and Bathwater!

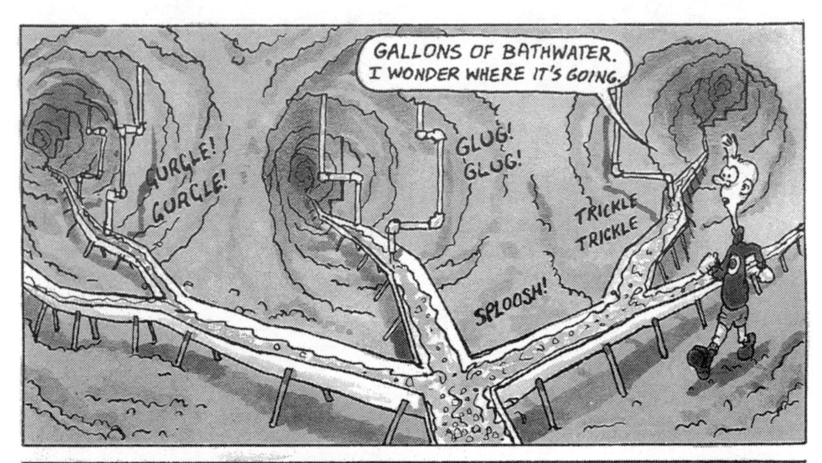
GALLONS OF BATHWATER. I WONDER WHERE IT'S GOING.
GURGLE! GURGLE!
GLUG! GLUG!
TRICKLE TRICKLE
SPLOOSH!

BLIMEY! WHAT'S THIS? WATER RECYCLING?
POUR!
SPLISH! SPLASH!

CREEAK!

CREEAK!
CREEAK!

BLIMEY!

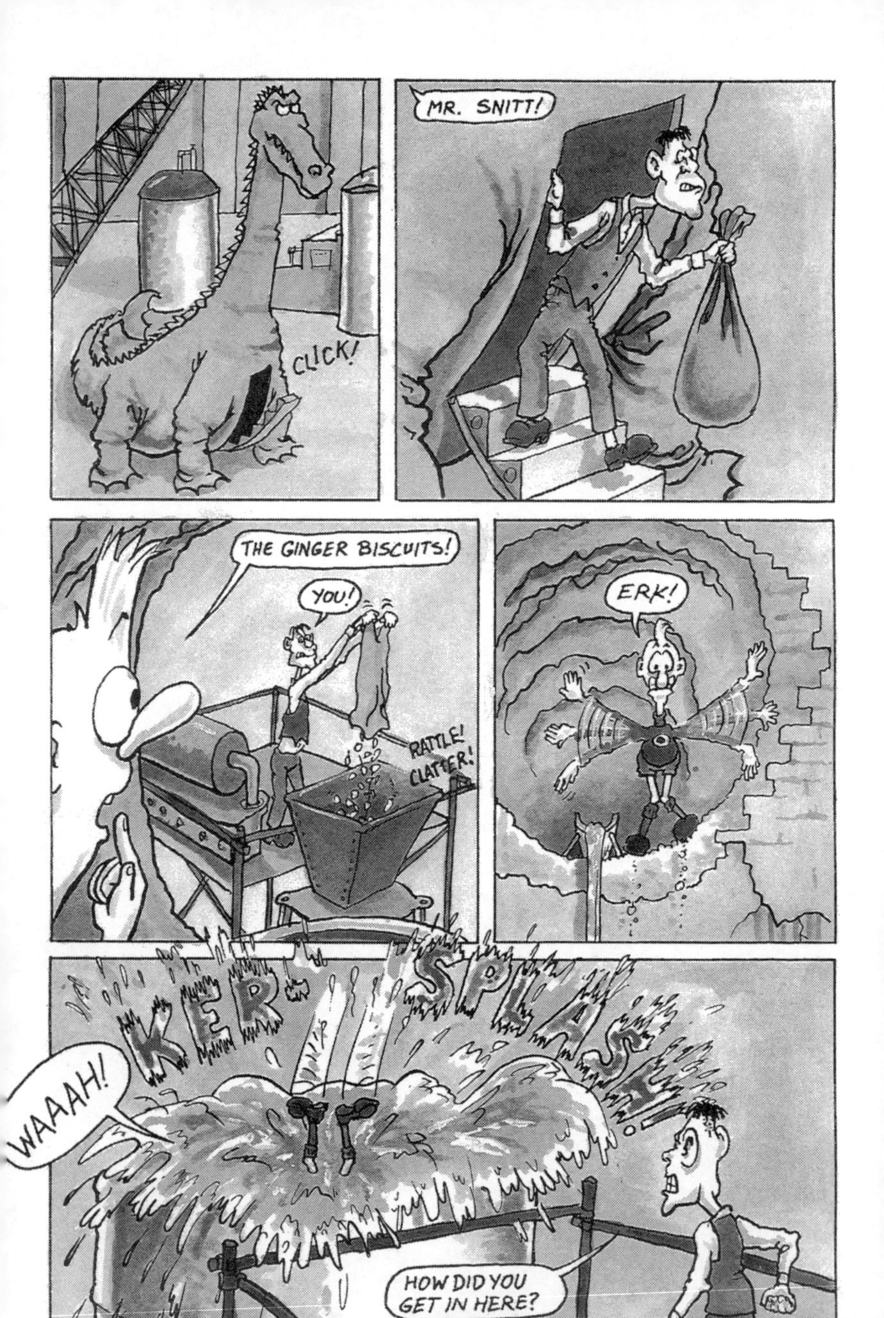
CLICK!
MR. SNITT!
THE GINGER BISCUITS!
YOU!
RATTLE! CLATTER!
ERK!
KER-SPLASH!
WAAAH!
HOW DID YOU GET IN HERE?

YOU MAY AS WELL KNOW IT ALL. I'VE GOT NOTHING TO LOSE. A FEW YEARS AGO, I STARTED FILLING GINGER BEER BOTTLES WITH BATHWATER AND GINGER BISCUIT CRUMBS TO MAKE CHEAP FAKE GINGER BEER.

YUCK!

SOON THE SHOP WAS FAMOUS, AND MAKING LOTS OF MONEY. I WAS USING ALL MY BATHWATER, AND STILL THERE WASN'T ENOUGH, SO I BOUGHT A DIGGING MACHINE AND DUG TUNNELS RUNNING UNDER ALL THE BATHS IN THE VILLAGE TO COLLECT THE BATHWATER I NEEDED.

THIS IS THE CELLAR OF THE OLD MONASTERY. IT WAS AN IDEAL PLACE TO HIDE THE MACHINES I NEEDED TO MAKE ALL THIS GINGER BEER.
SNITT'S WINKLETHORPE GINGER BEER
SNITT'S WINKLETHORPE GINGER BEER

BUT I HAD A PROBLEM. I WAS SPENDING TOO MUCH ON GINGER BISCUITS TO MAKE THE CRUMBS. I DECIDED TO STEAL THE BISCUITS I NEEDED. SO I REBUILT THE DIGGING MACHINE AND COVERED IT WITH THIS DISGUISE. IF ANYBODY SEES IT, THE POLICE WON'T BELIEVE THEM.

THE MONSTER IS ALSO SUPPOSED TO SCARE PEOPLE OFF. UNFORTUNATELY, IT DIDN'T WORK ON YOU, SO YOU'RE GOING TO HAVE TO DISAPPEAR.

DISAPPEAR?

SAD, BUT NECESSARY FOR NOSY LITTLE KIDS LIKE YOU. IT'S TIME FOR A LITTLE EVENING STROLL.

THIS HAS RUINED MY SHOES, YOU KNOW.
I WOULDN'T WORRY ABOUT THAT IF I WERE YOU!

IT'S LOW TIDE NOW. SOON THE SEA WILL COME IN AND YOU'LL BE HISTORY. THEN THERE WILL BE NO-ONE TO STOP IT!
STOP WHAT?

MY MASTER PLAN! BOTTLED BATHWATER IS ONLY THE BEGINNING!
I'LL SELL SPONGECAKES MADE WITH USED BATH SPONGES!
BOOTLACE LIQUORICE MADE WITH BOOTLACES!
IF YOU THINK SCHOOL DINNERS ARE BAD, JUST WAIT UNTIL I START MAKING THEM! IT'LL MAKE ME RICH! FILTHY RICH! I'LL BE A MILLIONAIRE! HAH!

SO I'M TAKING NO CHANCES! GOODBYE!
BYE!

AND DON'T BOTHER TRYING TO HOLD YOUR BREATH!

WHAT AN OLD MISERY GUTS!

SHOULDN'T BE ALLOWED TO RUN A TEASHOP!
POP!

THIS IS TOO HEAVY TO CARRY! I'LL HAVE TO LEAVE IT AND GO FOR HELP!

SO-
KATE! KATE!

SHHH! YOU'LL SCARE THE MONSTER AWAY!

WHAT'S HAPPENED TO YOUR FEET?
THE MONSTER IS A FAKE! COME AND SEE!

ORSON TELLS KATE THE STORY–
SO MY FEET ARE STUCK SOLID IN THIS BUCKET OF CEMENT!

HANG ON! I KNOW JUST WHAT WE NEED!

SOON–
READY?
O.K. TURN IT ON!

CAREFUL! THEY'RE THE ONLY FEET I'VE GOT!

OOOH! THAT'S BETTER! LET ME GET THEM BACK ON AGAIN!

'ELLO, 'ELLO, 'ELLO! WHAT'S ALL THIS 'ERE THEN?

THAT DRILL'S COUNCIL PROPERTY, THAT IS.
WE'VE FINISHED. WE JUST BORROWED IT FOR A MINUTE

WE'VE GOT SOMETHING TO TELL YOU, TOO!
IS THAT SO?

YES! YOU KNOW THAT SEA MONSTER THAT STOLE THE GINGER BISCUITS? WELL, IT WAS REALLY MR. SNITT FROM THE TEASHOP, AND HE TRIED TO DROWN ME BY STANDING ME IN A BUCKET BECAUSE I KNEW HE WAS PUTTING CRUMBS IN THE BATHWATER, BUT I GOT AWAY BECAUSE MY FEET CAME OFF!

YES, OF COURSE. WELL, IF THAT'S ALL, I'LL BE GOING, THEN.
?

BUT IT'S TRUE!

WELL, DO YOU HAVE ANY - AHEM! PROOF OF THIS STORY?
YES!

THIS IS THE BUCKET!
WELL, YES. IT IS A BUCKET. I CAN SEE THAT. BUT I'M NOT CONVINCED.

NOW, IF YOU BRING ME THIS SEA MONSTER, THAT WOULD BE DIFFERENT. GET ON HOME, BOTH OF YOU. GOODNIGHT!

WHAT ARE WE DOING HERE?
THIS IS WHERE THE GINGER BEER FACTORY IS. IF WE FIND THAT MECHANICAL MONSTER, THE POLICE WILL HAVE TO BELIEVE US.

BUT HOW ARE WE GOING TO GET IT? THE DOOR IS LOCKED!

YES, LOCKED FROM THE INSIDE. AND THE KEY'S STILL IN IT. THE MONSTER MUST BE THERE.

WHAT SHOULD WE DO?
I'VE GOT AN IDEA!

THERE'S JUST ROOM FOR MY HAND.

POP!

CLICK!

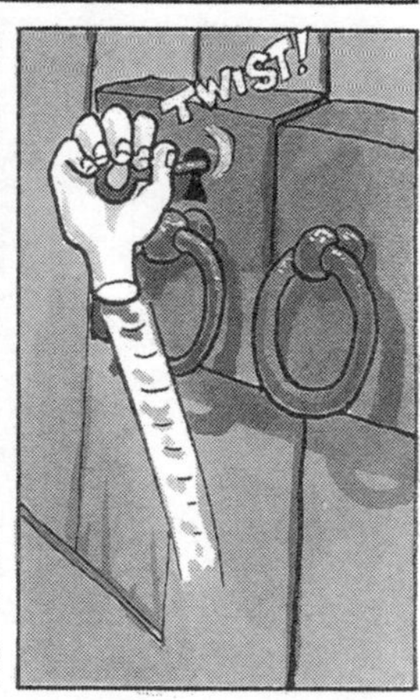
TWIST!

CREEEAK!
SHHHH!

CREEP! CREEP!

THERE IT IS!

THERE'S A DOOR
IN IT SOMEWHERE.

HEY! YOU!

BLIMEY! IT'S HIM!
QUICK! GET IT OPEN!

STOP!
GET IN!

SLAM!

INSIDE-
BLIMEY! SOMETHING MUST MAKE IT GO!
TRY EVERYTHING!

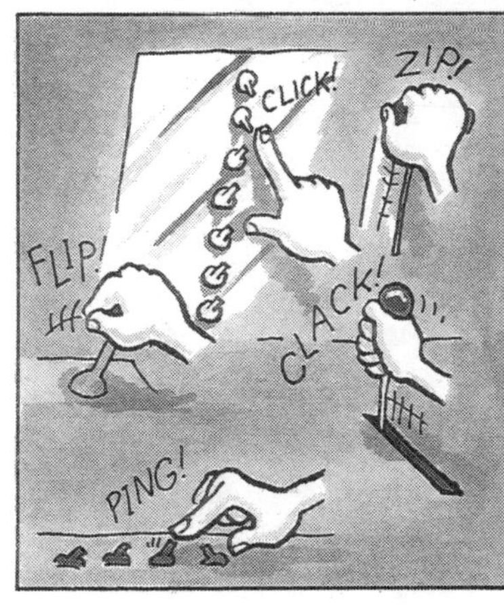
CLICK!
ZIP!
FLIP!
CLACK!
PING!

BINGO!

WHICH WAY DO WE GO?
HOW DO I KNOW? I CAN'T SEE OUT!

I'LL GET YOU! I'LL GET YOU BOTH FOR THIS!!
BANG!
BANG!

HERE! TRY THIS PERISCOPE!

GRRRR!
HELP! BACKWARDS! FAST!

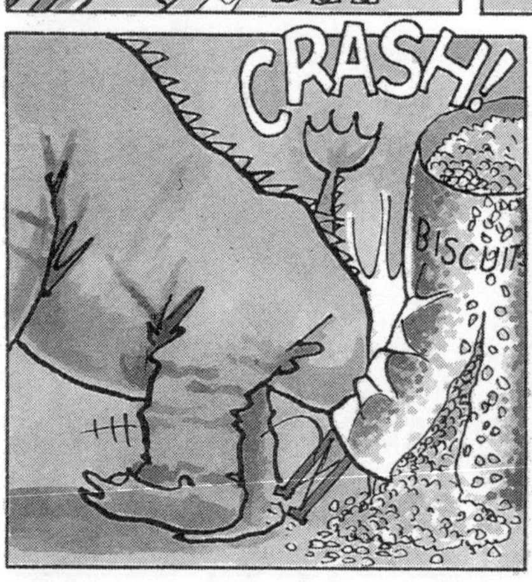
CRASH!
BISCUITS

WHAT WAS THAT?
NEVER MIND! TURN LEFT - I THINK!

BUMP!
SPLOOSH!

YOU LITTLE... GLUB! GLUB! GLUB!

AH! THERE'S THE DOOR - BUT WE SHUT IT ON THE WAY IN!

FULL SPEED AHEAD!

KERRUNCH!!!

KEEP GOING STRAIGHT ALONG THE BEACH! WE'RE HEADING FOR THE VILLAGE!

THIS'LL FIX 'EM!

KAPWINNNG!
BANG!

WHAT WAS **THAT?**
HE'S GOT A **GUN! FASTER!**

I THINK WE'VE LOST HIM.

SUDDENLY—
WHAT'S HAPPENING?
THUD!

OH, NO!
OUR OWN MONSTER TRAP!

HE'LL FIND US IN HERE!
STAY DOWN. HE MAY GO PAST.

THUD! THUD! THUD!
THAT DOESN'T SOUND LIKE MR. SNITT'S FOOTSTEPS!

MUNCH MUNCH
BLIMEY! A **REAL** SEA MONSTER!

JUST THEN-
?
GOT YOU!
? ?

COME OUT OF THERE NOW!
THUMP!
THUMP!

THIS IS YOUR LAST CHANCE!

EH?... AAAAARGH!
GRAB!

IT... IT CAN'T BE!
SWALLOW!

'ELLO, 'ELLO, 'ELLO, WHAT'S ALL THIS DISTURBANCE, THEN?
HELLO!

WELL, BLOW ME DOWN! A SEA MONSTER!
BURP!
BOOM!

I THINK YOU'D BETTER ARREST MR. SNITT : WE'VE GOT ALL THE EVIDENCE!
YES! LOCK ME UP NOW! YOU'VE GOT TO!

AND WHY MIGHT THAT BE, SIR?
THIS GREAT BEAST'S GOING TO EAT ME!

YUCK!

NO! IT WANTS BISCUITS!
BISCUITS

I'LL CONFESS! JUST KEEP THAT THING AWAY FROM ME!
GOOD BOY!
HAVE SOME MORE!
MUNCH! MUNCH!
BISCUITS

EPILOGUE:
TEAS
BISCUITS FOR THE MONSTER
LIFE IS MUCH EASIER, NOW MR. SNITT HAS GONE. I CAN RUN THE SHOP BETTER BY MYSELF.
THE MONSTER CERTAINLY KEEPS THE CUSTOMERS COMING, DOESN'T HE?

YES! THE SHOP HAS NEVER BEEN SO FULL!

THAT *COULD* BE BECAUSE YOU'VE STOPPED SELLING SNITT'S GINGER BEER!
HA HA!

DO YOU THINK THE MONSTER WILL STAY?
I DOUBT IT.

HE'S SHY AT HEART, THAT'S WHY WE'VE NEVER SEEN HIM BEFORE. WHEN HE GETS TIRED OF BEING FAMOUS HE'LL GO BACK TO SEA AGAIN.

JUST FOR NOW, HE'S DOING WHAT YOU TWO ARE DOING.
WHAT'S THAT?
HAVING A HOLIDAY!
THE END.